Investigating the WEATHER

a project based laboratory manual

SECOND EDITION

Kendall Hunt
publishing company

Kennie Leet

www.kendallhunt.com
Send all inquiries to:
4050 Westmark Drive
Dubuque, IA 52004-1840

ISBN 978-1-7924-3515-7

Published in the United States of America

Contents

Preface

With the ever-increasing processing power of computers, technology in the field of meteorology is rapidly changing as well. The modern meteorology student, whether intending to pursue a career in meteorology or just taking the class to fulfill liberal arts electives, needs to have a basic understanding of where to consume real-time, accurate weather data used by scientists to generate forecasts and conduct research. Modern laboratory activities should be dynamic and engaging, students should be able to analyze what's currently happening in the world around them, and instructors should be able to direct students based on the day's current weather with the best meteorological data available. This provides both students and instructors with a unique experience each laboratory conducted, allowing for greater discussion of the events and nuances of each particular weather pattern. The emphasis of these activities is in the process, not finding a specific answer, of course there are correct and incorrect ways to do something, but this laboratory book is not static, the answers will change just as the weather changes. *Investigating the Weather: A Project-Based Laboratory Manual* is an introductory college-level laboratory manual comprised of three parts: **Part One: Activities in Observation, Part Two: Understanding Meteorological Concepts through "Real-Time" Data** and **Part Three: Hands-on Activities and Assignments.** Each lab activity in all these parts includes an **Introduction**, **Know Before You Go** pre-lab work, **Get the Data** procedure section, and **Apply Your Knowledge** conclusion section. A description of each section is below.

Part One: Activities in Observation includes five activities designed to increase the student's awareness of the weather around them. The activities in this section are designed to be spread out over the entire course and includes a Pre-Assessment, the first laboratory assignment of the course and a Post-Assessment, the last laboratory assignment of the course. These activities also include observation over several days and can be introduced as laboratory work or as assignments accompanying lecture material.

Part Two: Understanding Meteorological Concepts through "Real-Time" Data includes eight activities designed to use real-time or historically based data for a specific point in time to understand major concepts in meteorology. Many of the activities in this section are designed for traditional 2- or 3-hour laboratory sessions with some suggesting additional summary work outside of the laboratory, depending on the instructor's laboratory submission requirements.

Part Three: Hands-on Activities and Assignments includes three optional activities for use by instructors. These activities are easily used as assignments or incorporated into traditional laboratory time.

For the Student

The purpose of *Investigating the Weather: A Project-Based Laboratory Manual* is to engage you, the student, in the use of actual data in laboratory assignments, resisting the traditional pen and paper one-solution style laboratory manual. The assignments in this manual are dynamic and ever changing based on the day's weather and the region you are taking the course in. The focus is on the process and the journey so you can have a greater understanding of the types of weather data that is available and the complexity of the science of meteorology. Enjoy it and keep your eyes on the skies, you never know what you might observe!

For the Instructor

This laboratory manual is designed to accompany *A World of Weather: Fundamentals of Meteorology*, 6th Edition by Jon M. Nese and Lee M. Grenci. These activities have no set answer key, in using real-time data, the answers are always changing. This encourages student inquiry and increases student knowledge of weather data readily available online. The style of this also gives the instructor an opportunity to select an assignment based on the day's weather, is there a classic low-pressure system in the central United States? Jump to the surface weather maps activity and allow students to hand analyze the system in real time. My goal was to modernize the traditional introductory meteorology laboratory experience to produce more knowledgeable consumers of weather information and more inquisitive research minded students. Aside from the optional *Snowflakes* activity, there are no materials other than computers with Internet access required for these laboratories making them engaging in both traditional, online, and blended style learning modalities. Finally, several of these laboratories allow students to produce original material such as video blogs, narrated presentations, or other social media style reports to communicate current weather topics. Instructors have the ability to allow student freedom in this area or select a specific type of media to be used to summarize the weather data. With the growth of social media platforms, more and more meteorologists are reaching viewers on social media. Assignments of this nature allow students to experience the production that is involved in even a short weather post. Thank you and I hope you enjoy these activities!

Activities in Observation

Part

Weather Basics: A Preassessment

Laboratory

Introduction

Weather affects us every day, for some it's whether or not to wear a jacket or bring an umbrella, for others it can drive their entire day. With the increase of technology, many of us check the weather at least once per day via an app, a website, or even the morning news, but do we really remember what the forecast is? Do we understand why the weather is going to behave the way it is? Do we know if the forecasters are highly confident in the forecast or if the system is complex and a more challenging forecast?

This laboratory activity is designed to assess your current level of weather understanding and start familiarizing yourself with additional web resources for your weather information. The goal of the activities in observation are to increase your ability to observe the weather conditions around you and to become a better consumer of weather data.

Know Before You Go

Prior to completing the laboratory activity, you should review Chapter 1 Weather Analysis: Tools of the Trade in *A World of Weather: Fundamentals of Meteorology* and answer the following questions:

a. What is your current location? State the latitude and longitude of that location.

b. How many degrees of latitude is your current location from the Tropic of Cancer?

c. Based on your location, which map projection, polar stereographic or Mercator, do you feel would typically be used in your region? Why?

d. Based on your location, how much time do you need to add or lose to convert your time to Coordinated Universal Time (UTC)? How does Daylight Saving Time affect that conversion?

e. If the weather forecast lists an 80% probability of precipitation (POP), what does that mean?

f. What meteorological factors related to the precipitation are not included in the POP?

g. Look up your current conditions on your favorite weather app or website. Draw a surface station model with as much information as possible from your source, refer to Figure 1.24 Chapter 1 Weather Analysis: Tools of the Trade in *A World of Weather: Fundamentals of Meteorology*. List the source data next to your station in a simple table.

h. What is the definition for dew-point temperature?

Get the Data

Throughout this section, you will access websites, primarily those operated by the National Weather Service and answer questions about the information you find. Remember the goal of this laboratory activity is to get acclimated to the daily weather resources available and access your current knowledge of the forecast and basic weather information. If you are unsure, don't be afraid to say that. By the end of the semester, you will work through a very similar assignment with much greater ease.

1. Begin by finding your local National Weather Service webpage, the easiest way to accomplish this is to go to www.weather.gov and then click on your location.
   a. Every office's page is set up a little different so you may find it helpful to spend a few minutes just navigating the links and getting used to the way the information is presented for that office.
2. Find the "Current Conditions" tab and if there is a drop-down box, select "Observations." You should see a map with weather symbols indicating the present weather in your region. Right-click the map and save a copy, you will include this in your lab report.
   a. List the conditions at the station model closest to your current location.

   b. Describe any overall trends or patterns you see in the current conditions, be as descriptive as possible.

3. Go back to your National Weather Service office homepage, find the current surface weather map. You will see large blue Hs and red Ls along with other symbols on this map. Right-click the map and save a copy, you will include this is your lab report.
   a. What type of projection is this map?

   b. What date and time was this map generated, as listed on the map? What date & time is this in your local time?

   c. Over what states do you see high pressure?

   d. Over what states do you see low pressure?

   e. What types of fronts are present on this map? And where are they? What do they mean for upcoming weather?

f. Is rain forecasted in any part of the United States? If so, what states? With what type of pressure system do we find the precipitation?

4. Go back to your National Weather Service office homepage again, find the "Hour-by-hour" forecast chart, it will look very similar to the meteograms described in Chapter 1 in *A World of Weather: Fundamentals of Meteorology*. Save the chart for your report.

a. Is this an observation or forecast meteogram?

b. How do temperature and dew-point temperature change over the next few days?

c. What is the trend in relative humidity over this same time period?

d. Is surface wind expected to change over the next few days? If so, how?

e. What is the Precipitation Potential over the next 48 hours? What is the highest percentage forecasted?

f. How does pressure change over the next 48 hours?

5. Go back to your National Weather Service office homepage, under the "Forecast" heading, choose the "Forecasters' Discussion." Save a copy of the current discussion. The forecasters' discussion can be rather dense and daunting but it is by far the best place to get an objective view of what the forecaster is thinking and why. Often in this discussion, the forecasters will discuss if the different forecast models (computerized simulations of how the atmosphere will change, used to predict future weather) are handling the weather situation very well. Read through the discussion as best as you can.

a. How long ago was this forecast discussion generated?

b. Do the forecasters seem confident in the upcoming weather forecast? Why or why not?

c. What challenges exist in the forecast?

Apply Your Knowledge

Answer the following questions based on the data you have collected above.

1. Based on what you have read and discovered, write a short summary of the current weather conditions in your area. If instruments or a local weather station is available, your instructor may ask you to also view and record observations at your current location.

2. Based on what you have read and discovered, write a short summary of the forecasted weather conditions for your area.

3. What is the advantage in looking at current conditions using station models rather than a table of weather data?

4. On the surface weather map, what is a front? How are fronts represented?

5. On the meteogram, do you notice a relationship between relative humidity and dew point over the forecast period?

6. On the meteogram, how does temperature change day versus night? Is that expected? Why or why not?

Cloud Types and Optical Phenomena: Visual Observations

Laboratory

2

Introduction

Weather, especially in the Northeastern United States, can vary greatly day to day. Through careful observation and attention to the atmosphere around us, we can begin to learn clues about upcoming weather based on the changes we see. Not too long ago, meteorologists took careful observations of the low-, middle, and high-level clouds each and every hour. With advances in satellite technology, the need for hourly cloud records has disappeared. Despite this change, careful observation of the world around us is still a valuable skill to possess and one that can be improved with practice. This laboratory activity will encourage you to look around you and observe with more detail what you see and feel. As you work on these observations, think about what you are learning in class, and how what you see and feel relates to that material.

In order to complete this lab, you should have a basic working knowledge of the basic cloud types. Figure 2.1 shows the vertical heights of the basic cloud types.

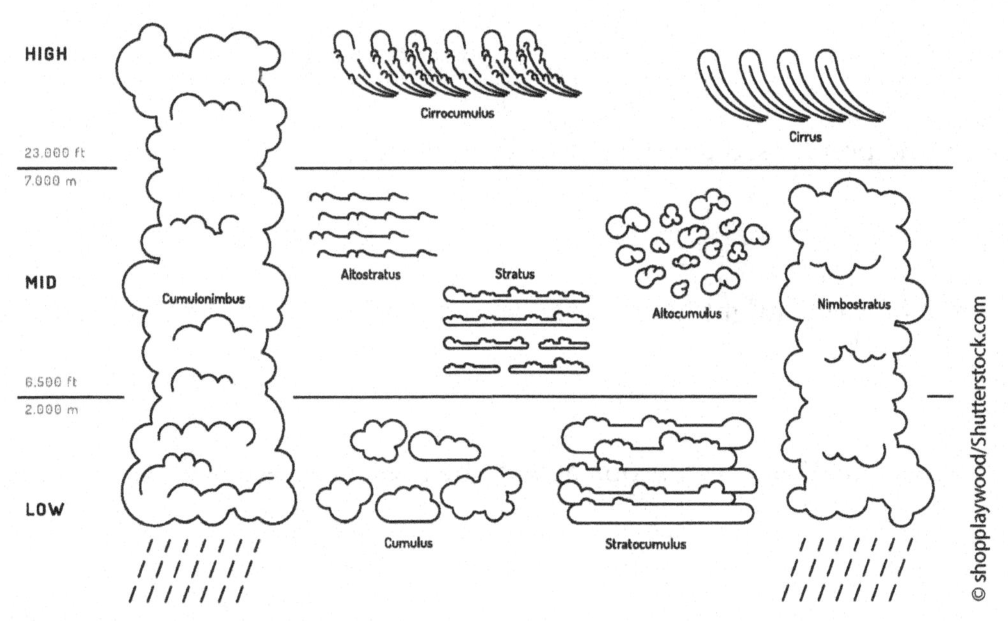

Figure 2.1. Cloud types.

Know Before You Go

Prior to completing the laboratory activity, you should review the end of chapter "Focus on Optics" sections and Chapter 4 The Role of Water in Weather in *World of Weather: Fundamentals of Meteorology*. In addition to the textbook readings, review the National Weather Service page on the Four Core Cloud types (https://www.weather.gov/jetstream/core-four) and the Ten Basic Clouds (https://www.weather.gov/jetstream/basicten). Additionally, the National Weather Service provides a nice color cloud chart (https://www.weather.gov/media/jetstream/slouds/cloudchart.pdf). In addition to cloud types, you may also observe interesting atmospheric phenomena throughout the week. I encourage you to visit https://www.atoptics.co.uk/ to familiarize yourself with some of the phenomena that occur in the atmosphere prior to beginning any observations.

a. What is the similar word used to describe high clouds? What are high clouds primarily composed of?

b. How would you best describe a cumulus cloud? What is the key component of cumulus clouds?

c. What is the prefix or suffix used to describe precipitation in low clouds?

d. What is the prefix used to define mid-level clouds?

e. Describe how one might identify various types of stratus clouds.

f. What is a halo? What conditions need to be present in order for an observer to view a halo?

g. What conditions need to be present in order for an observer to view a rainbow?

h. What times of day are crepuscular rays typically observed? Why? (Refer to Chapter 1 in *World of Weather*)

Get the Data

1. For 5 consecutive days, make at least two observations at different times of day. Each observation should include
   - **a.** Photograph of the sky/clouds, be sure to include landmarks, buildings, and such, for perspective and scale
   - **b.** Date, time, and location
   - **c.** Current weather conditions (temperature, dew-point temperature, relative humidity, pressure, and any precipitation) from nearest reliable source, state source
   - **d.** Describe the current weather conditions in your own words
   - **e.** Identify any and all clouds and optical phenomena you observe, discuss why you are selecting that specific cloud type
   - **f.** Optional: Add a visible satellite map from near the same time as the cloud observation, zoom in to your region if possible
2. Compile your data into a document that is well organized and includes all of the above information.

Apply Your Knowledge

1. Choose one cloud type observation and describe any connections you can make between the cloud type and the observations you made for that day.

2. As you look at the 5-day period on the whole, focusing on cloud types, what overall trends do you observe about the entire week?

3. Atmospheric optical phenomena can be rarely observed; if you were lucky enough to photograph and capture a phenomenon, please describe it here. If you did not capture any unique phenomena, please visit https://www.atoptics.co.uk/ and choose a feature to describe. List and describe it.

4. What do you think went well with this project?

5. What would you do differently if you were to observe the clouds and atmosphere again in this manner?

Laboratory

3

Daily Weather Maps: An Analysis

Introduction

Weather maps provide a quick, easy-to-read spatial analysis of atmospheric conditions. The most common weather map is the surface weather analysis. Surface weather maps assume a constant height surface, typically sea level, and plot the barometric pressure changes throughout the region of interest. This analysis allows the reader to quickly resolve high- and low-pressure systems, fronts and other key atmospheric surface conditions. Upper air maps are also used in conjunction with surface maps to resolve the day's expected weather conditions. Upper air maps are analyzed at constant pressure levels and analyzed for changes in height of the pressure surface. On upper air maps, we look for ridges and troughs, jet stream positions, and cold or warm air advection, just to name a few of the key indicators. Through observation of weather maps over the course of several days, we can begin to see changes in the evolution of weather systems as they track across the United States.

Know Before You Go

Prior to completing the laboratory activity, you should review Chapter 1 Weather Analysis: The Tools of the Trade in *World of Weather: Fundamentals of Meteorology*, Chapter 6 Surface Patterns of Pressure and Wind in *World of Weather: Fundamentals of Meteorology*, and Chapter 7 Upper air Patterns of Pressure and Wind in *World of Weather: Fundamentals of Meteorology*.

a. When isobars are tightly packed, we call this a high gradient, on a surface weather map, what can we say about the expected surface wind speed?

b. What type of weather might be expect when high pressure is dominating a region?

c. What upper air feature is associated with a surface low-pressure system?

d. Around which type of pressure system would we expect to see frontal boundaries?

e. On what upper air height map would we expect to find the jet stream?

f. How does one look for warm- or cold-air advection on an upper air map? Which level should we use to find advection?

Get the Data

1. Go to the National Oceanic and Atmospheric Administration surface weather map analysis at http://www.wpc.ncep.noaa.gov/sfc/usfntsfcwbg.gif. Save this image, you may be asked to include it in a final laboratory report or laboratory submission.
   a. Describe the weather map in your own words, where are the high and low-pressure systems, are there any fronts present, what type and where are they located.
2. Go to the National Center for Atmospheric Research at http://weather.rap.ucar.edu/upper/, look for the Winds/Temps at Pressures including contours list and select the following: 850 mb, 500 mb, 300 mb. Save and label the images as you may be asked to include them in a final laboratory report or laboratory submission.
   a. On the 850-mb map, look for areas of warm and cold air advection. Label or describe in what regions they are present that day.
   b. On the 500-mb map, look for ridges and troughs. Label or describe in what regions they are present that day.
   c. On the 300-mb map, look for the strongest winds and determine the location of the jet stream. How might the jet influence surface weather that day.
3. Repeat Steps 1 and 2 for 5 consecutive days.

Apply Your Knowledge

1. Where were the major high-pressure systems at the start of your observation? How or where did they move by the end of your observation?

2. Where were the major low-pressure systems at the start of your observation? How and where did they move by the end of your observation?

3. Describe the movement of the major frontal boundaries throughout your time period of study.

4. For your location, describe the movement of the high and low-pressure systems and fronts throughout your 5-day period.

5. Describe the weather you experienced during the same 5-day period. How did your weather relate to features you observed on the weather maps? (Think about high- and Low-pressure systems, fronts, warm and cold air advection, ridges and troughs, and the jet stream)

6. Can you make a general statement about the association of warm and cold air advection to specific surface map features? Said another way, where do you typically find warm and cold air advection?

7. Were there any major changes in the jet stream throughout the observation time period? If so, describe them.

Optional Assignment

Present your summary of the daily weather maps throughout your time period studied in a social media style update format. Organize the information into a 2-minute or less summary of the week's weather. Use a Facebook live (first person webcam video) or narrated Powerpoint Presentation style, your instructor will provide more details if this option is required.

Laboratory 4

Forecasting: Comparing Sources and Accuracy

Introduction

Have you ever checked the weather forecast on Monday, read it was going to be an excellent weekend, and made plans only to forget about the weather the rest of the week and find you are rained out that weekend? Or now, with apps on our phones and tablets, do you check the weather daily but find you don't know much beyond the sun or rain icon? This laboratory activity is designed to look beyond the icons and 10-day forecast summaries. As a part of the observation laboratory section, this activity will have you observe the forecast and weather over a longer time period.

Phone with weather app.

Know Before You Go

Prior to completing the laboratory activity, you should review Chapter 17 Numerical Weather Prediction in *World of Weather: Fundamentals of Meteorology*, Chapter 17 is available online at https://www.e-education.psu.edu/worldofweather/ and answer the following questions.

a. Describe how meteorologists use pattern recognition in generating forecasts.

b. What is the NAM? What are the spatial and temporal scales for the NAM?

c. What are some of the challenges with forecasting beyond 3 or 4 days as described by the authors in *World of Weather*?

Get the Data

1. Using your favorite Internet application or website find a 10-day forecast for your city. Write your forecast source below and the date and time you accessed it on.

2. Make a table including the daily high and low temperature, precipitation forecast and any other important details from your forecast source. Add a blank column or row to enter in the actual Daily High and Low Temperature, Precipitation, and so on. See Table 4.1 for an example.

3. Access the 10-day National Weather Service forecast for the same city as Step 1. Include a column/row in your table for the NWS forecast and a column/row for the actual Daily High and Low temperature, precipitation, and so on if the NWS forecast does not go out 10 days, please use as many days as are listed.

4. Write a paragraph to explain the upcoming weather in your own words.

5. In your opinion, which forecast gave you more information about the upcoming weather over the next 10-day time period?

6. Did either of your sources give the same level of detail throughout the 10-day time period? If not, explain the differences you observed.

7. Go to the National Weather Service Forecasters Discussion of the forecast office that covers your city. Based on the Forecasters Discussion, what is the confidence the forecasters have for the upcoming forecast? If confidence is low, summarize why the forecasters might have low confidence in the upcoming forecast.

8. What time period does the Forecasters Discussion cover? Does it match with your forecast time period?

9. Over the next 10 days, fill in the column of your table with the actual daily high and low temperatures, and so on, then complete the Apply Your Knowledge section. These should be recorded from the National Weather Service, go to your local National Weather Service Homepage and select the Climate and Past Weather area, click on "Observed Past Weather". Here you will see options similar to Figure 4.1. Choose the date you are interested in and record the official maximum and minimum temperatures for that day.

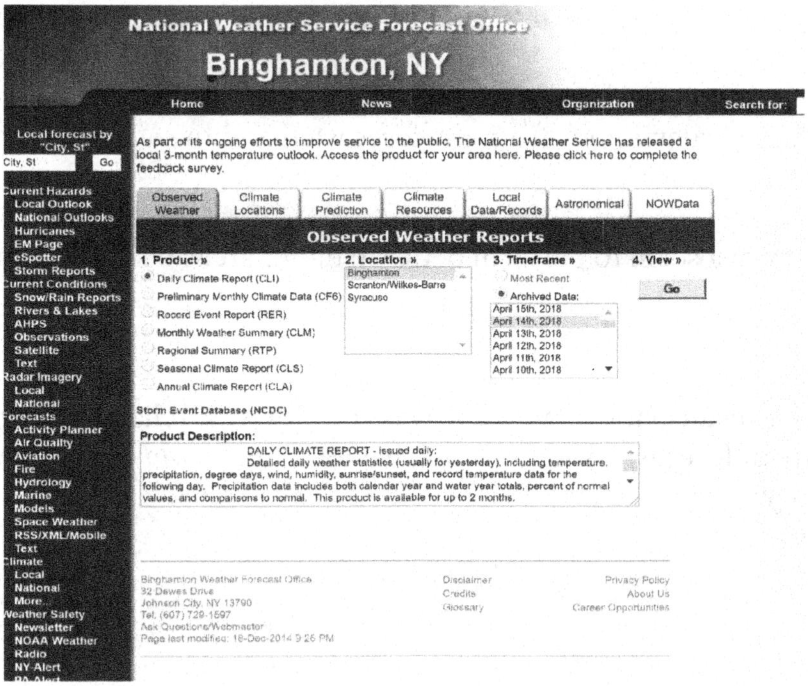

Figure 4.1. How to access observed weather reports from the National Weather Service.

Source: US Department of Commerce.

Apply Your Knowledge

1. How accurate were the forecasted temperatures you accessed in Step 1? State how you are determining the accuracy.

2. How accurate were the forecasted temperatures you accessed from the National Weather Service?

3. Explain any major deviations from the forecasted and actual temperatures (for instance, was an overnight low forecasted to be higher, but a cloud-free night cause temperatures to dip lower than expected).

4. How did accuracy change over the course of the 10 days?

5. Did any major weather patterns influence the accuracy? Explain.

6. How accurate was the forecasted precipitation information in Step 1?

7. How accurate was the National Weather Service precipitation information?

8. Explain any major deviations from the forecasted and the actual precipitation.

9. Did either forecast seem to perform better in either area? If so, which one and in which areas?

10. Based on your results, how many days was your forecast reliable? Does this match with the reliability of forecasts discussed in Chapter 17 in *World of Weather: Fundamentals of Meteorology*?

Table 4.1. Forecast Weather Observation Record

Source 1 (Internet/Application Forecast):						Date/Time Accessed:
Source 2 (National Weather Service):						Date/Time Accessed:
	Source 1 Max/Min Temperature	Source 2 Max/Min Temperature	Source 1 Precipitation	Source 2 Precipitation	Actual Max/ Min	Actual Precipitation
Day 1						
Day 2						
Day 3						
Day 4						
Day 5						
Day 6						
Day 7						
Day 8						
Day 9						
Day 10						

Laboratory

Weather Summary: A Postassessment

5

Introduction

A storm is moving into your area in the upcoming weeks, knowing you have been taking an introductory Meteorology class, your friend asks if you know anything about the upcoming forecast. Using the knowledge you have gained throughout the semester, you will be able to find and analyze weather forecast information that you can summarize for your friend.

This laboratory activity is designed to assess the knowledge you have gained throughout the semester. The goal of this activity is to review current weather information and updated forecasts in order to prepare your own summary of the current weather scenario and conditions.

Know Before You Go

Prior to completing the laboratory activity, you should answer the following questions:

a. In what city is your local National Weather Service forecast office located?

b. Briefly describe the areas your local National Weather Service office is responsible for in their forecasts.

c. What type of weather do you generally expect when there is high pressure at the surface?

d. What type of weather do you generally expect when there is low pressure at the surface?

e. How many days out are forecasts typically accurate for? Is this number consistent or are there scenarios where it could change?

Get the Data

Throughout this section, you will access websites, primarily those operated by the National Weather Service and answer questions about the information you find. This activity is very similar to Lab 1 and used to assess the knowledge gained throughout the semester.

1. Begin by finding your local National Weather Service webpage, the easiest way to accomplish this is to go to www.weather.gov and then click on your location.
   a. Every office's page is set up a little different so you may find it helpful to spend a few minutes just navigating the links and getting used to the way the information is presented for that office.
2. Find the "Current Conditions" tab and if there is a drop-down box, select "Observations." You should see a map with weather symbols indicating the present weather in your region. Right-click the map and save a copy, you will include this in your lab report.
   a. List the conditions at the station model closest to your current location.
   b. Describe any overall trends or patterns you see in the current conditions, be as descriptive as possible.
3. Go back to your National Weather Service office homepage, find the current surface weather map. You will see large blue Hs and red Ls along with other symbols on this map. Right click the map and save a copy, you will include this in your lab report.
   a. What type of projection is this map?

   b. What date and time was this map generated on?

   c. Over which states do you see high pressure?

   d. Over which states do you see low pressure?

   e. What types of fronts are present on this map? And where are they? What do they mean for upcoming weather?

   f. Is rain forecasted in any part of the United States? If so, for which states? With what type of pressure system do we find the precipitation?

g. How will you expect your weather to change in the upcoming days based on what you observe on the surface map?

4. Go back to your National Weather Service office homepage again, find the "Hour-by-hour" forecast chart, it will look very similar to the meteograms described in Chapter 1 in *World of Weather: Fundamentals of Meteorology*. Save the chart for your report.
   a. Is this an observation or forecast meteogram?

   b. How do temperature and dew-point temperature change over the next few days?

   c. What is the trend in relative humidity over this same time period?

   d. Is surface wind expected to change over the next few days? If so, how?

   e. What is the Precipitation Potential over the next 48 hours? What is the highest percentage forecasted?

   f. How does pressure change over the next 48 hours?

   g. How does the information on the meteogram relate to what you observed on the surface map (Question 3g.)?

5. Go back to your National Weather Service office homepage, under the "Forecast" heading, choose the "Forecasters' Discussion." Save a copy of the current discussion. The forecasters' discussion can be rather dense and daunting but it is by far the best place to

get an objective view of what the forecaster is thinking and why. Often in the discussion the forecasters' will discuss if the different forecast models (computerized simulations of how the atmosphere will change used to predict future weather) are handling the weather situation very well. Read through the discussion as best as you can.

a. How long ago was this forecast discussion generated?

b. Do the forecasters seem confident in the upcoming weather forecast? Why or why not?

c. What challenges exist in the forecast?

Apply Your Knowledge

Answer the following questions based on the data you have collected above.

1. Based on what you have read and discovered, write a short summary of the current weather conditions in your area. If instruments or a local weather station is available, your instructor may ask you to also view and record observations at your current location.

2. Based on what you have read and discovered, write a summary of the forecasted weather conditions for your area.

3. How do the station model plots of current weather relate to any fronts or pressure systems in your area today? Are any major changes expected over the next few days?

4. On the surface weather map, over which states do you see fronts? List the type and locations, it may be helpful to make a table.

5. On the meteogram, do you notice a relationship between relative humidity and dew point over the forecast period?

6. On the meteogram, if a front is forecasted to pass by your location, what indications of the frontal passage can you discern from the meteogram?

Understanding Meteorological Concepts through "Real-Time" Data

Part II

Current Weather: Meteograms and Station Models

Laboratory

Introduction

How much do you remember when you look at a table of numbers? Is it easy to spot trends and changes quickly? Meteorologists need to process a lot of data rapidly. This data needs to have spatial and temporal connotation. Meteorologists process data quickly through the use of weather charts and maps. Meteograms are used to gain quick information about the changing weather variables for one geographic point; this gives the reader a temporal look at the weather variables for one particular location. Figure 1.30 Chapter 1 Weather Analysis: The Tools of the Trade in *World of Weather: Fundamentals of Meteorology* shows a standard meteogram for Fargo, North Dakota, during the 25-hour period beginning at 11 UTC on January 19, 2013. What information can you quickly gather from looking at this meteogram? Weather maps are used to gain quick information about the spatial variation in weather patterns over a large region but often is fixed on one point in time (now with the use of advanced computer processing we can easily advance hour by hour to see changes to the weather variables on the spatial scale). In this lab, we will plot the weather map data using hand-plotting techniques so we will set our map to one particular point in time. Note the changing weather variables over time. Figure 1.28 Chapter 1 Weather Analysis: The Tools of the Trade in *World of Weather: Fundamentals of Meteorology* shows station models in the south eastern United States plotted from 00 UTC April 28, 2011. Observe the changes in wind speed and direction ahead of and behind the cold front (blue line with triangles pointing in direction of motion). What information can you quickly gather from looking at this map?

Know Before You Go

Prior to completing the laboratory activity, you should review Chapter 1 Weather Analysis: The Tools of the Trade in *World of Weather: Fundamentals of Meteorology* and answer the following questions.

a. Draw a station model using the following information:
Temperature: 76°F
Dew-point Temperature: 61°F
Wind Direction: 210°
Wind Speed: 9 knots
Cloud Cover: Broken (5/8)
Pressure: 1022.0 mb

b. Decode the station model in Figure 1.27 in Chapter 1 Weather Analysis: The Tools of the Trade in *World of Weather: Fundamentals of Meteorology* to list the weather conditions this city is currently experiencing.

c. On the meteogram in Figure 1.30 in Chapter 1 Weather Analysis: The Tools of the Trade in *World of Weather: Fundamentals of Meteorology* What do the following represent:
Green line:
Top purple line:
Blue line:
Lower purple line:

d. On the meteogram in Figure 1.30 in Chapter 1 Weather Analysis: The Tools of the Trade in *World of Weather: Fundamentals of Meteorology,* where would I look to find information about winds and cloud cover? What changes do you notice over the 48-hour time period in Figure 1.30?

Get the Data

Station Models: Analyzing Spatial Data

1. Figure 6.1 is a blank map of New York State labeled with several of the larger cities. The cities are labeled with their three-digit airport code.
2. Look up the current weather observation data for New York State by going to https://www.aviationweather.gov/metar?gis=off on the right-hand side of the page you'll see a headline titled "Request METAR data," below that is an entry box: "IDs"; in that box, enter K + the three-digit airport code and click the radial button before "Decoded" then click "Get METAR data." Enter the data into Table 6.1. Repeat for each city on your map.
3. The first column is the three-letter station ID for the city listed in the second column Table 6.1. If you've ever flown out of one of these New York State cities, you'll notice the station ID is the same as the airport code plus the letter K in front. Our local airport slogan is "Think BGM first," you'll notice BGM is the three letters that stand for

Table 6.1. New York State Weather Observations

Date and Time of Observations:

Station ID:	City:	Temperature: (°F)	Dew-point Temperature: (°F)	Wind Direction:	Wind Speed:	Cloud Cover:	Pressure: (mb)
KLGA	Laguardia						
KPOU	Poughkeepsie						
KBGM	Binghamton						
KITH	Ithaca						
KELM	Elmira						
KALB	Albany						
KGFL	Glens Falls						
KSYR	Syracuse						
KRME	Utica-Rome						
KJHW	Jamestown						
KBUF	Buffalo						
KIAG	Niagara Falls						
KROC	Rochester						
KART	Watertown						
KPBG	Plattsburgh						
KFZY	Fulton-Oswego						

Table 6.2. Example information for KLGA Laguardia, data from 16 Z 25 July 2007

Station ID:	City:	Temperature: (°F)	Dew-point Temperature: (°F)	Wind Direction:	Wind Speed:	Cloud Cover:	Pressure: (mb)
LGA	Laguardia	81	59		Calm	SCT	1022.0

Binghamton, NY. On your NY state plot map, you'll also see city circles labeled with the three-letter station code. This saves space on your map.

4. In order to plot the information listed in the table above, you need to follow these instructions; you may also refer to Chapter 1 Weather Analysis: The Tools of the Trade in *World of Weather: Fundamentals of Meteorology.*
   a. All of your plotting is to be done in PENCIL! Mechanical pencils are preferred because you can usually write a bit smaller.
   b. Plotting should be NEAT; take your time and write small but legible. The station information should fit under the size of a nickel.
   c. Temperature is listed in Fahrenheit and is plotted in the upper left-hand corner of the station circle. We'll use your first city, LGA as an example. If the station name or map lines are in the way, just adjust the value slightly up, down, left or right.

81

   d. Dew-point temperature is related to temperature and tells us something about the amount of moisture in the air. Dew-point temperature is given in Fahrenheit and is listed below the temperature in the lower left-hand corner.

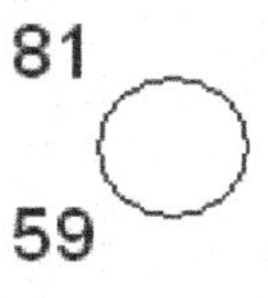

   e. Wind direction is given in degrees. You are probably more familiar with North, South, East, West, and so on, but here we use the degree value to

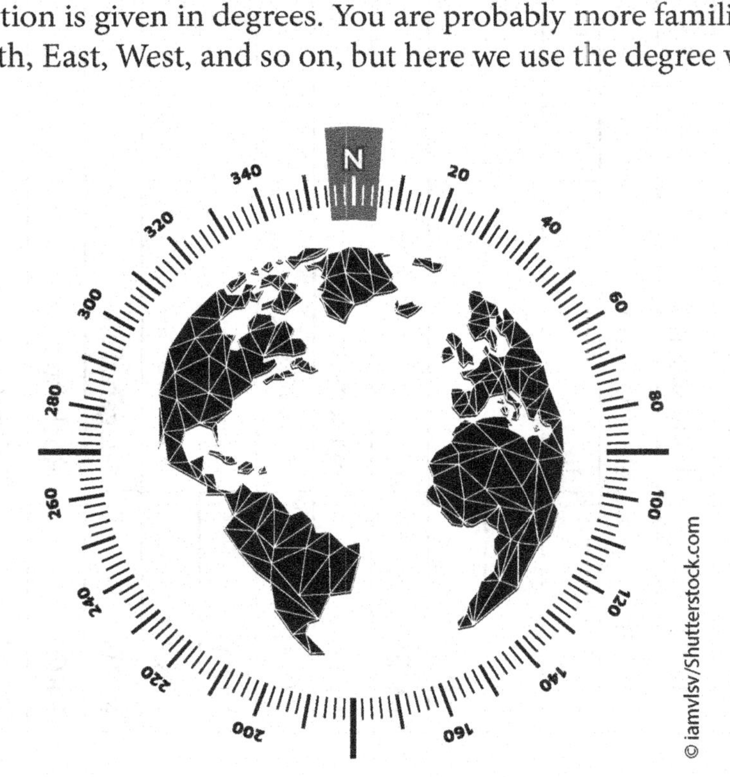

© iamvlsv/Shutterstock.com

represent the direction. This diagram below will help you determine whereabouts the degree number is found.

If no direction is given, then the city is experiencing calm winds. Calm winds are labeled by simply drawing a circle around the station circle shown on your map. LGA would now look like this:

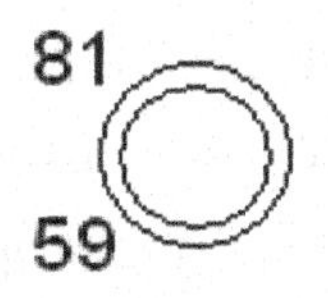

But what if your city has a wind direction and speed given? The wind direction would be plotted by drawing a line extending out from the station circle along that degree line. For instance, let's say LGA had a wind direction of 90°. This is what the city plot would look like:

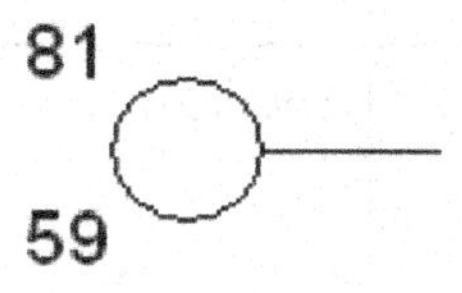

Now for the direction, in our true example of LGA, there was no wind direction so we simply had to draw the circle around the station, but let's say that LGA had a wind direction of 90°, which is shown above and a wind speed of 10 knots. To show that the wind was blowing 10 knots, we would draw a wind barb pointing clockwise off of the wind direction line. Wind barbs represent the wind speed. 10 knots would look like this in LGA:

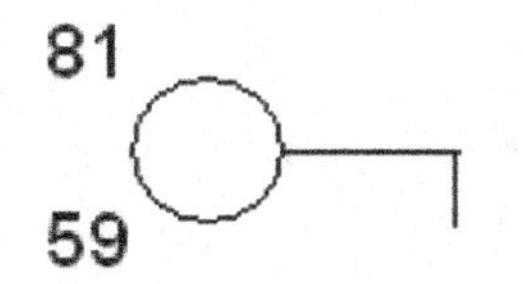

Wind barbs are drawn differently depending on the wind speed, refer to Table 6.3 or Figure 1.24c Chapter 1 Weather Analysis: The Tools of the Trade in *World of Weather: Fundamentals of Meteorology.*

Table 6.3. Wind Speed Station Plot Examples

Wind Barb	Wind Speed
	Half Barb, represents wind speeds around 5 knots
	Full Barb, represents wind speeds around 10 knots
	Flag, represents wind speeds around 50 knots

You can use the table above in any combination. A 25-knot wind would be represented like so:

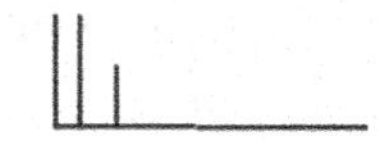

f. Cloud cover is plotted by shading in the center of the station circle. Use Table 6.4 or Figure 1.24b Chapter 1 Weather Analysis: The Tools of the Trade in *World of Weather: Fundamentals of Meteorology* as a guide:

Table 6.4. Cloud Cover Plotting Examples

Abbreviation	Cloud Cover	Shading on Map
CLR	Clear	None
SCT	Scattered	
BRK	Broken	
OVC	Overcast	

This would mean LGA would now look like this:

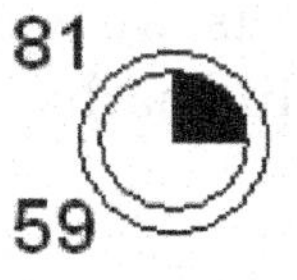

g. The final variable to plot is pressure. The pressure is given to you in millibars (mb) and you'll notice that all of the pressures are around 1000 mb. Our maps would get cluttered if we plotted all of the numbers, so we need to shorten the pressure or put it into code. To code pressure, we simply drop the 9 or 10 in front and drop the decimal point. Pressure code should always be three digits—even if it's all zeros. It helps to begin by making sure all of your pressures have just one decimal place. For LGA, we need to drop the 10 and the decimal to be left with 220.

1022.0

Finally, our plot of LGA should look like this:

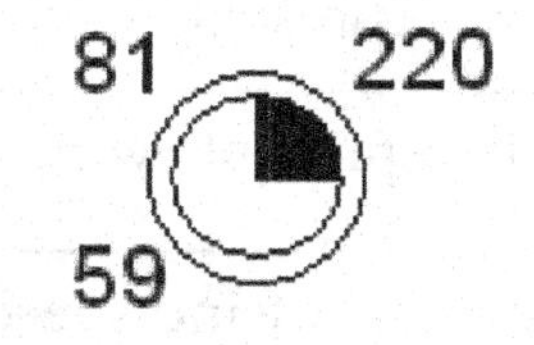

h. Now repeat these steps and plot all of the cities given for New York State on the Figure 6.1 map.

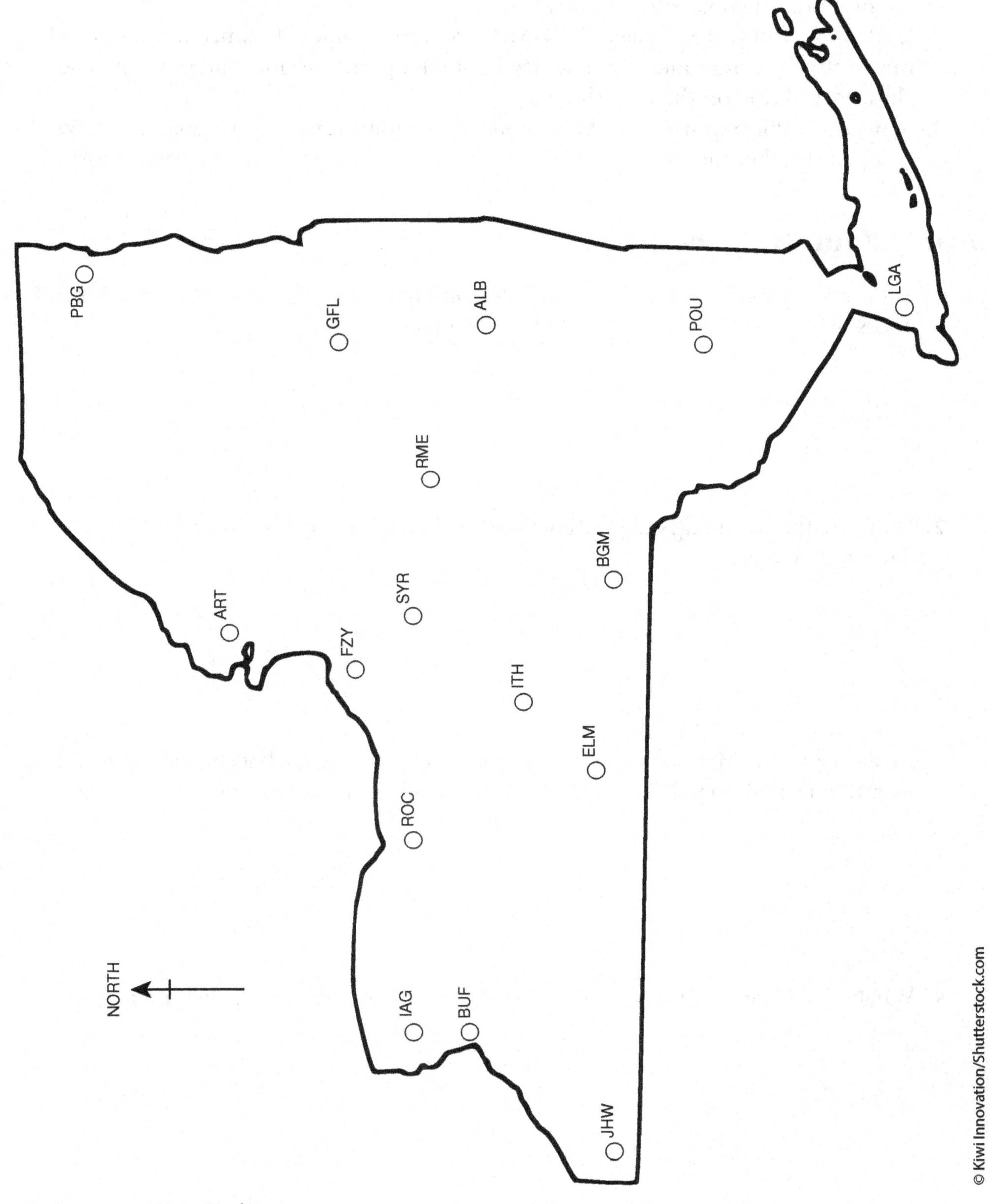

Figure 6.1. New York state.

Meteograms: Analyzing Temporal Data

1. Go to http://weather.uwyo.edu/surface/meteorogram/index.shtml and click on your region under "Global Surface Data."
2. Under "Type of Output" select "GIF Meteorogram." Under Station, enter K+ your local three-letter airport code, you may need to look up this number, alternatively you may click on a station on the map shown.
3. A new tab will pop up with the current Meteogram for that city, copy and save this image to another file, you may be asked to submit it with your laboratory report.

Apply Your Knowledge

1. Looking at the station models you plotted on Figure 6.1, what are some weather differences that you can notice across New York State?

2. What are the advantages to plotting weather data on the map versus simply reading the data from a table?

3. In observing the Meteogram you saved for the city selected, what changes do you notice over the next 48 hours? Be specific, describe each variable if needed.

4. What advantages do you have in observing the upcoming weather using a meteogram?

Laboratory

Prevailing Winds: Wind Roses and Applications

Introduction

Wind roses are constructed to help visualize common wind speeds and direction data over a specified time period. Figure 10.6 in Chapter 10 Tropical Weather, Part I: Patterns of Wind, Water, and Weather in *A World of Weather: Fundamentals of Meteorology* shows a wind rose example from Rapid City, SD. Remember winds are measured in the direction the wind is blowing from. This means when a meteorologist tells us today's wind direction is south, we can make an inference about what the temperature and conditions might be for that day. Here in the northeast, a south wind usually brings with it warmer and more humid air. If we were expecting winds to change to north, how might you expect temperature to change? You should also notice on the Rapid City wind rose that the triangular "petals" that indicate wind direction are all different lengths. What does the length of the petal tell the reader? The longer the petal, the more frequent the wind comes from that direction. Wind speed on the Figure 10.6 in Chapter 10 Tropical Weather, Part I: Patterns of Wind, Water, and Weather in A *World of Weather: Fundamentals of Meteorology*" is indicated by color. Figure 10.7 in Chapter 10 Tropical Weather, Part I: Patterns of Wind, Water, and Weather in A *World of Weather: Fundamentals of Meteorology* shows two separate charts, one for wind direction, the wind rose and one for wind speed, a bar graph.

Know Before You Go

Prior to completing the laboratory activity, you should review Chapter 10 Tropical Weather, Part I: Patterns of Wind, Water, and Weather in *A World of Weather: Fundamentals of Meteorology* and answer the following questions.

a. What is meant by prevailing wind?

b. In Figure 10.6 in Chapter 10 Tropical Weather, Part I: Patterns of Wind, Water, and Weather in *A World of Weather: Fundamentals of Meteorology,* what is the prevailing wind for Rapid City, SD?

c. In Figure 10.7 in Chapter 10 Tropical Weather, Part I: Patterns of Wind, Water, and Weather in *A World of Weather: Fundamentals of Meteorology* what is the frequency of winds observed coming from 120°?

Get the Data

1. Access wind rose data for a specific month for your nearest city, the data is for the years 1961–1990.
   a. Go to the US Department of Agriculture Natural Resources Conservation Service website at https://www.wcc.nrcs.usda.gov/climate/windrose.html.
   b. Click on "Wind Rose Dataset."
   c. Click on the state of your nearest station.
   d. Click on the nearest city.
   e. Select one .gif file for each season, that is, a winter month, summer month, spring month, and fall month.
   f. Save and/or print each file.
2. Access wind rose data on a long-term, annual basis for your nearest city.
   a. Go to Iowa State University, Iowa Environmental Mesonet page at https://mesonet.agron.iastate.edu/sites/locate.php.
   b. In the drop-down box to the right of "Select by Network" change the network to your state + "ASOS," click "Switch Network."
   c. In the drop-down box to the right of "Select by Station," change the station to your nearest station, click "Select Station."
   d. Choose "Wind Roses," (Note you could also enter custom dates if you had a particular research question to answer by selecting "Custom Wind Roses."
   e. The top image displayed in the Yearly Climatology for the selected city. Record the following from that image:
      i. Location:
      ii. Period of Record:
      iii. Prevailing Wind:
      iv. Average Wind Speed:
      v. Percentage of time that location is calm:
   f. Print and/or save the image.

Apply Your Knowledge

1. Summarize the prevailing wind for the months you selected in "Get the Data" Step 1. Did you observe any differences based on time of year? What are some possible reasons for these seasonal differences?

2. Wind roses have very practical applications when it comes to city and urban planning, pollution crisis management, and so on. Using the wind rose you accessed in "Get the Data" Step 2, cut out the image in Figure 7.1a–e, and affix them with glue or tape to your wind rose at the best possible location. For instance, where could you place the factory so the pollution does not fumigate the city? We'll assume the city's downtown area is right at the center of your wind rose. (Try not to cover up the wind petals.)

3. Write a short paragraph discussing some of the challenges with planning your city and why you placed certain items in certain places.

4. Analyze your city planning. Again, use the wind rose you created in "Get the Data" Step 2. Look up a detailed map for the city you selected. Sketch the important components of the city (industrial area, residential areas, large parks or topographic changes, educational, and medical facilities). Now think about a major atmospheric pollution event, train accident, or factory emission. Based on the prevailing wind in your city, where might that pollution travel and who might be impacted? (Obviously, in case of a real emergency, real-time wind data would be used but this information is often used in city planning for potential emergencies) We also have a case in our local area where on hot summer days, the prevailing winds push the smell from the sewage treatment plant into a large residential area so the application of these wind roses can be very beneficial to urban planning!

Figure 7.1a. Factory icon./Heavy Industrial.

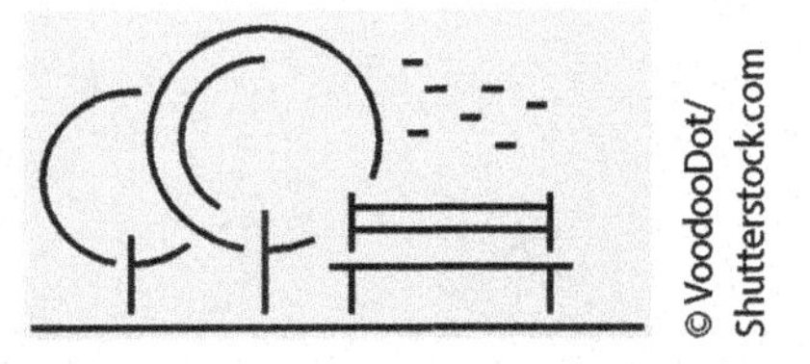

Figure 7.1b. Nature icons/Parks and Recreation.

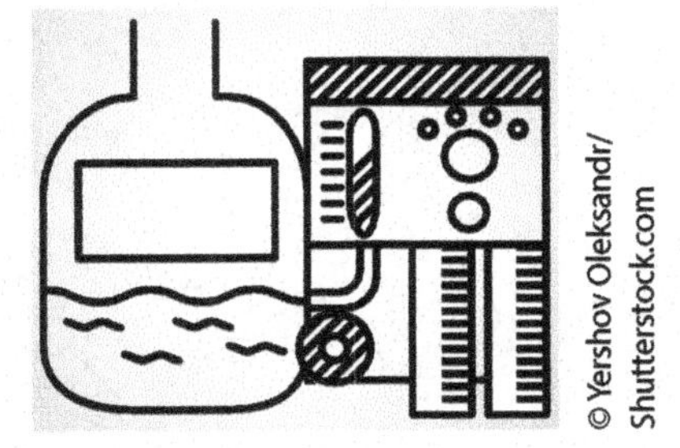

Figure 7.2c. Sewage treatment Facility.

Figure 7.3d. Various homes/Housing Development.

Figure 7.4e. School.

Controls of Climate: Comparing United States Cities

Laboratory

8

Introduction

The temperature of a city throughout the year is controlled by four major variables. These variables are the cities proximity to water, latitude, and elevation. Large bodies of water modify a city's climate by moderating the annual temperature range. Annual temperature range is defined as the temperature difference between the highest average monthly temperature and the lowest average monthly temperature. Coastal cities have low annual temperature ranges, therefore, little change in temperature throughout the year. Also, cities along the ocean coast can be further modified by the ocean water just offshore. Ocean currents transport large amounts of energy that influence broader regional climate, Figure 8.1 shows the

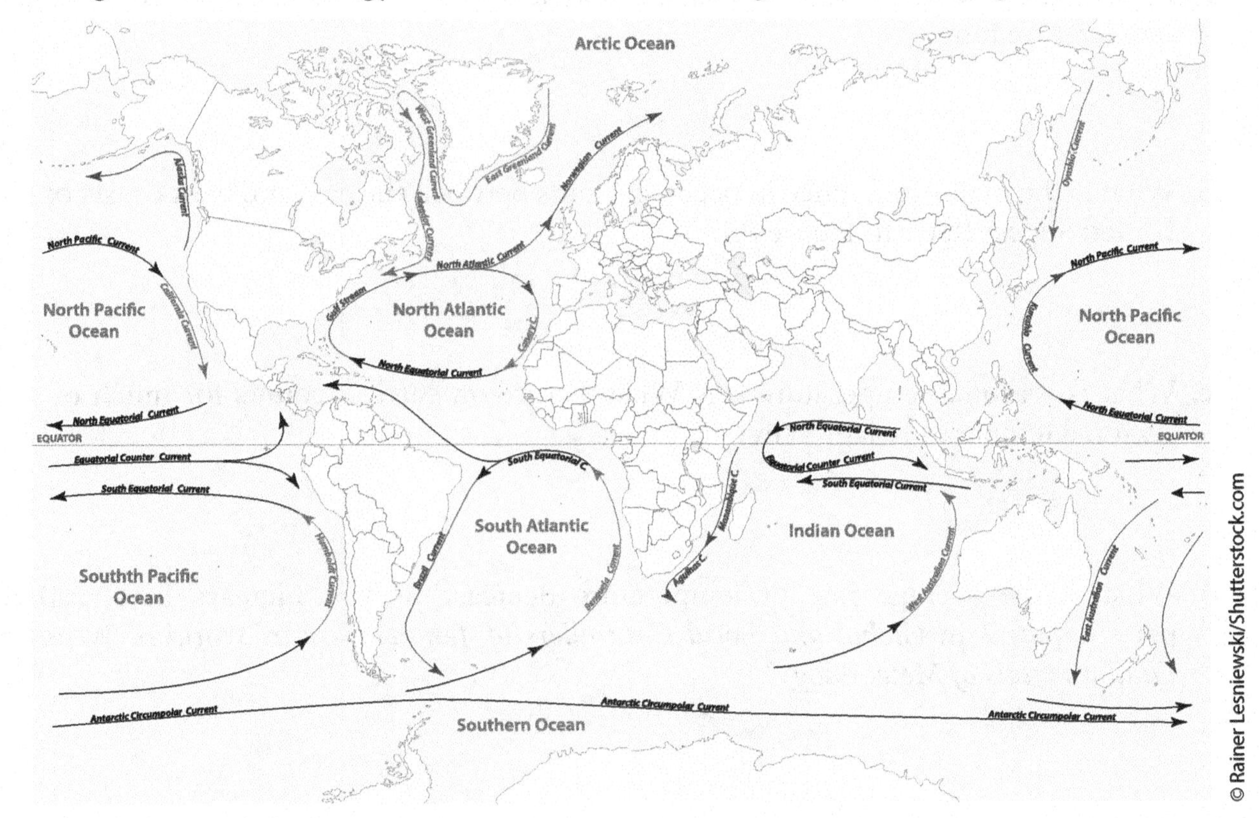

Figure 8.1. World map currents.

major global ocean currents and their direction of flow. Interior cities have greater swings in temperature between the warmest and coldest months, therefore high annual temperature ranges. As we have learned from Chapter 2 The Global Ledger of Heat Energy in *A World of Weather: Fundamentals of Meteorology*, the angle of incoming solar radiation also plays a large role in affecting a city's annual temperature. Higher latitude cities have lower angles of incoming solar radiation and therefore have lower average annual temperature. Average annual temperature is the average of average monthly temperatures throughout one year for a city. Elevation can also influence a city's annual temperature changes by lower the average annual temperature. This lab will explore these concepts through the use of readily available climate data.

Know Before You Go

Read Chapter 2 The Global Ledger of Heat Energy and Chapter 3 Global and Local Controllers of Temperature in *World of Weather: Fundamentals of Meteorology* and answer the following questions.

a. Explain the concept of specific heat capacity as it relates to modifying a city's annual temperature range.

b. What is the major difference in ocean currents between the east and west coasts of the United States? Refer to Figure 8.1.

c. What is seasonal temperature lag? What feature on earth accounts for much of our seasonal temperature lag? Why?

d. What is the average rate of temperature decrease as you increase in elevation, per Chapter 3 in *Global and Local Controllers of Temperature* in *World of Weather: Fundamentals of Meteorology*?

Get the Data

1. Go to www.usclimatedata.com. This website provides a simple look at a city's annual temperatures. You will use this website for all data collection in this laboratory activity. Please also refer to Figure 8.2 Physical Map of the United States or another United States map for assistance in choosing cities for this activity.

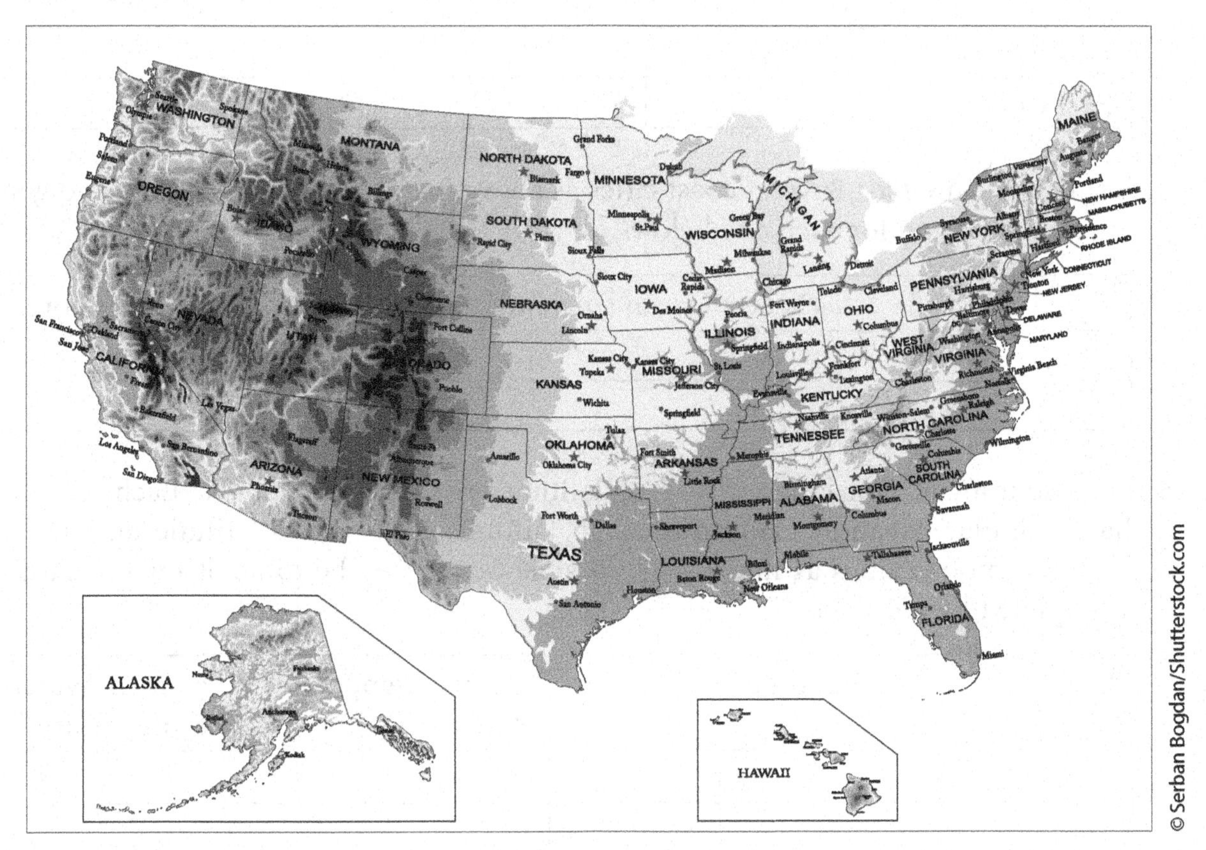

Figure 8.2. US map.

2. Choose one coastal and one interior city to compare the influence of a large body of water. Keep in mind you want to keep other variables as similar as possible so the two cities you select should have similar elevations and similar latitudes. Write the cities you selected, below. Calculate the annual temperature range and list the average annual temperature for each city, below.

	City:	Elevation:	Latitude:	Annual Temperature Range (°F):	Annual Average Temperature (°F):
Coastal:					
Interior:					

3. Now choose two coastal cities, one on the west coast of the United States and other on the east coast. As before, be sure to keep other variables constant, the cities should be at a similar latitude and elevation. Write the cities you selected, below and each city's annual average temperature.

	City:	Latitude:	Elevation:	Annual Average Temperature (°F):
West Coast:				
East Coast:				

4. Using the same East & West coast cities as above, name the ocean current and general current direction for each city below.

City:	Closest Ocean Current:	General Current Direction:

5. Choose four interior cities at varying latitudes in the United States. Each city should have a similar elevation. Choose one high-latitude city, two mid-latitude, and one lower latitude; choose cities as interior as possible but it may be difficult for low latitudes. Complete the table below.

City:	Latitude:	Elevation:	Annual Temperature Range (°F):	Annual Average Temperature (°F):

6. Finally, we need to see how elevation impacts a city's temperature. For this comparison, choose two cities that are relatively close to one another but at very different elevations, elevations should be several thousand feet difference, the larger the difference, the more variation you will observe. As always, all other variables should be similar, similar in proximity to water and latitude. Complete the table below.

	City:	Elevation:	Latitude:	Average Annual Temperature (°F):
Mountain:				
Valley:				

Apply Your Knowledge

1. How did the proximity to a large body of water influence the temperature of the two cities you selected?

2. What was the average annual temperature for your east and west coast cities? Were your results surprising? Why or why not? What explains this difference?

3. What influence did latitude have on the four cities you selected? How did average annual temperature vary from your highest to your lowest latitude city?

4. How did elevation affect the two cities you selected? How does your difference compare to the typical decrease in temperature with increasing elevation (from "Know Before You Go" Step D)?

5. Did any of your results surprise you? Can you use any of the other variables to explain any anomalies?

6. If you were planning to travel to any of these cities, what information from the www.usaclimatedata.com city pages could assist you planning what to pack for that time of year? Be specific about the data you might use and why that would be the best indication of climate in that region.

Surface Weather Maps: Isoplething and Interpretation

Laboratory

9

Introduction

We have all seen the classic surface weather map with red Ls and blue Hs representing low and high pressure, respectively with fronts plotted to show location and direction of movement. These surface weather maps provide the reader with a quick, easy way to interpret regional or national weather. Isoplething is the process of creating lines of equal value like contouring on topographic maps, see Chapter 1 Weather Analysis: The Tools of the Trade in *World of Weather: Fundamentals of Meteorology* for a review of contouring. On surface weather maps, we create isobars, lines of equal pressure. Isobars allow us to determine locations of high and low pressure. The standard convention is to plot isobars every 4 mb, for instance, lines would be plotted at 996 mb, 1000 mb, 1004 mb, 1008 mb, and so on up or down depending on the daily values. This laboratory assignment will have you access to surface weather plots in real time and conduct the analysis. Mesoscale meteorologists at the Storm Prediction Center still use hand analysis techniques for storm forecasting.

Know Before You Go

Prior to completing the laboratory activity, you should review Chapter 6 Surface Patterns of Pressure and Wind in *World of Weather: Fundamentals of Meteorology* and answer the following questions.

a. What type of wind speeds do we expect when the pressure gradient force is high?

b. How does friction influence surface winds around high & low pressure systems?

c. What are the vertical and surface characteristics of a high-pressure system?

d. What are the vertical and surface characteristics of a low-pressure system?

e. What conditions are expected ahead of and behind a cold front?

f. What conditions are expected ahead of and behind a warm front?

Get the Data

1. Go to the Storm Prediction Center Surface Map page at http://www.spc.noaa.gov/exper/surfaceMaps/.
2. Below the United States map, select "Contiguous United States" (unless there is an interesting current regional weather pattern and you are directed to focus on a specific region).
3. Print out the map.
4. Using a 0.5-mm mechanical pencil, analyze the map by creating isobars every 4 mb. (Remember pressure is plotted in code, see Chapter 6 in *Surface Patterns of Pressure and Wind in World of Weather: Fundamentals of Meteorology* for a refresher on how to go between coded pressure and actual pressure. Be sure to label the isobars in a clear and easy-to-read way as you would typically find on a surface weather map.
5. Label any high-pressure systems with a blue H.
6. Label any low-pressure systems with a red L.
7. Identify and label any major fronts. Be sure to use standard convention for color and shape.

Apply Your Knowledge

1. Based on the surface weather map, what weather do you expect in your region today?

2. Based on the surface weather map, how might your weather be changing over the next 24 hours?

3. What did you find challenging about isoplething?

4. What did you learn by doing this analysis by hand?

Upper Air Maps: Contouring and Interpretation

Laboratory

10

Introduction

Upper air charts are extremely useful for forecasting and general understanding of atmospheric conditions. We are used to television meteorologists focusing on surface weather and changes in surface atmospheric conditions, but rarely to look at the atmosphere in the vertical dimension. The atmosphere, like the Earth, is not flat. Upper air atmospheric conditions influence surface conditions and vice versa. You will learn much more about these interactions throughout the course. This laboratory assignment uses access to real-time upper air data to introduce you to upper air charts and allow you to hand analyze three of the mandatory pressure levels and determine the day's upper air conditions.

Know Before You Go

Prior to completing the laboratory activity, you should review Chapter 7 Upper Air Patterns of Pressure and Wind in *World of Weather: Fundamentals of Meteorology* and answer the following questions.

a. What is meant by mandatory pressure levels?

b. What are the mandatory pressure levels?

c. What is a trough? How is it delineated on a weather map?

d. What is a ridge? How is it delineated on a weather map?

e. What does a pronounced southward dip (trough) indicate on a 500-mb chart?

f. What does a pronounced northward bulge (ridge) indicate on a 500-mb chart?

g. In addition to height, what else do we plot on a 300-mb chart? Why?

h. How would we find a strong pressure gradient force on a map?

i. What is zonal flow?

j. What is meridional flow?

k. What is cold- or warm-air advection?

Get the Data

1. Go to The National Center for Atmospheric Research Real-Time Weather Data page for upper air data at http://weather.rap.ucar.edu/upper or spc.noaa.gov/obswx/maps/

2. Across from "rawinsonde plot at" select 850 mb, 500 mb, and 300 mb. Print each chart.

3. Analyze each chart by drawing contour lines with 0.5 mm mechanical pencil. On the 850-mb map, draw contour lines 30-m intervals 1500 m, 1440 m, and so on. On the 500-mb map, draw contour lines in 60 m intervals, conventional contours include 4980 m, 5400 m, 5640 m, and so on. On the 300-mb map, draw contour lines at 120 m intervals, including 9120 m, 8880 m, 8640 m, and so on. (Be sure to plot all relevant isolines not just those listed above.)

4. On the 850-mb map, add isotherms, lines of constant temperature at 4°F intervals, clearly label the lines.

5. On the 850-mb map, label areas of cold and warm air advection. Refer to Chapter 13 Mid-Latitude II: The Cyclone Model in *World of Weather: Fundamentals of Meteorology* if needed for additional information on cold- and warm-air advection. We want to see areas where the isotherms are perpendicular to the contour lines (cross-cut), you can also look for perpendicular wind barbs. These are regions where warmer or colder air is being advected, moved by the wind, into that region.

6. On the 500-mb map, label any ridges and troughs.

7. On the 500-mb map, label regions of zonal flow.

8. On the 500-mb map, label regions of meridional flow.

9. On the 300-mb map, draw circular isotachs, lines of constant wind speed at 10-mph intervals only for winds greater than 100 knots.

Apply Your Knowledge

1. Based on the upper air map, what weather do you expect in your region today?

2. Based on the upper air map, how might your weather be changing over the next 24 hours?

3. Over what states did you observe the jet stream? Label it on your 300-mb map.

4. How does the position of the jet stream affect the upcoming weather? (*Note*: you may want to review the forecast on www.weather.gov.

5. What did you find challenging about isoplething and contouring?

6. What did you learn by doing this analysis by hand?

Role of the National Weather Service: A Virtual Field Trip

Introduction

Due to practical reasons, a tour of your local National Weather Service office is not always possible. A virtual field trip is the next best option to learn about the important role of the National Weather Service, and how it differs from other forecasts. This laboratory activity will have you explore several National Weather Service websites to learn more about this agency and your local office.

Know Before You Go

Review basic information about the National Weather Service at https://www.weather.gov/about/ and answer the following questions:

a. What is the mission of the National Weather Service?

b. What does Weather-Ready Nation mean in your own words?

Review the History of the National Weather Service at https://www.weather.gov/timeline and answer the following questions:

a. In the late 1800s, daily weather maps were created at which institution?

b. In which year did official 3-day forecasts begin?

c. What is the name for the professional organization of meteorologists that began in 1920?

d. In which year did the Weather Bureau commission the first WSR-57 Weather Surveillance Radar?

e. In which year was the world's first weather satellite launched?

f. In which year did the US Weather Bureau become the National Weather Service?

g. Which governmental organization oversees the National Weather Service?

h. In 1989, more than $4.5 billion was spent to overhaul and modernize the National Weather Service. Which five major changes arose from that investment?

Get the Data

Visit a local National Weather Service homepage Norman, Oklahoma office, www.weathergov/oun/office. Take the virtual tour and navigate the links about that office. Answer the following questions to the best of your ability based on the information you find:

1. Describe the counties, cities, and states the Norman, OK office forecasts for.

2. How many hours per day are forecasters on site?

3. Which airports is this office responsible to provide aviation forecasts for?

4. Does this site launch daily weather balloons for upper air information? If not, can you find the closest office that does?

5. Approximately how many people are employed at this office? Of that how many are meteorologists?

6. Who else besides meteorologists are employed at the National Weather Service?

7. How often are text/official forecasts updated at this office?

8. Describe one notable event in this office's history.

Visit the Faces of the National Weather Service page at https://www.weather.gov/careers/meteorology and answer the following questions.

1. What are the education and experience requirements for federal meteorology jobs?

2. At the bottom of the webpage are biographies and interviews with several National Weather Service employees. Choose one and answer the following questions.
   a. Name and title of individual chosen

   b. What is their educational background?

   c. Where do they work?

   d. What advice do they have for someone seeking a similar career?

Visit the National Weather Service www.weather.gov homepage and find your local office.

1. Where is the office located?

2. What is the forecast area for this office?

Apply Your Knowledge

1. In your own words, what is the primary function of the National Weather Service?

2. What surprised you most from your research about the National Weather Service?

Tornadoes: Conditions for Development

Introduction

The United States is home to some of the most active weather in the world, in the form of tornadoes. The central United States is home to Tornado Alley, a region where conditions are ideal for tornado formation and home to the highest number of tornadoes in the world. This lab uses the National Oceanic and Atmospheric Administration (NOAA), National Weather Service's Storm Prediction Center archives to learn more about the conditions needed for supercells and ultimately tornadoes to form through the analysis of a past mesoscale severe storm event. The Storm Prediction Center (SPC) is located in Norman, Oklahoma with the goal of providing the premier resource for timely and accurate severe weather forecasts and information. Find out more about the products the SPC provides by visiting their website at www.spc.noaa.gov.

Know Before You Go

Prior to completing the laboratory activity, you should review Chapters 9 Thunderstorms 14 Mid-Latitude III: Spawning Severe Weather and Chapter 15 A Closer Look at Tornadoes in *World of Weather: Fundamentals of Meteorology* and answer the following questions.

a. How do you define a supercell?

b. What are the four "ingredients" required to generate supercells?

c. Using an Internet search engine, library reference book, or other methods, look up three different tornado events that occurred in the United States between 2000 and present day. List the three potential events here. The goal will be for each student or group to cover a different event.

Get the Data

1. Choose one of the events above for your focus. Your instructor may assist with this process to ensure different events are covered or may direct the entire class to one particular event. List your event here:

2. Go to the NOAA National Weather Service Storm Prediction Center Archive page at http://www.spc.noaa.gov/exper/archive/events/.

3. Search for your event using the year, month, day, state search boxes. Click "Retrieve Events," Click on your event listed.

4. On the main page, you should see a map with dots indicating the location of storm reports during your event and below that a table of each storm report. Summarize the storm reports for your event, note the most severe damage.

5. On the left-hand side of the page, you will see a bluish-purple table with headings such as "SVR Reports," "Obs and Mesoanalysis," "Upper Air Analyses," "Skew-T/Log-P Charts," and so on. Click through these reports, maps, and information. Give yourself a general overview of the information you can find for your event.

6. Using the ingredients for a supercell from the "Know Before You Go" section, find charts, maps, or other information that demonstrates each of the ingredients for your day of the storm. Save any important images.

Apply Your Knowledge

1. Share your knowledge of this event with others by preparing a Video Blog, Text Blog, or Powerpoint presentation of your event, your instructor may provide further information, be sure to include the following:
   a. Timeline of the event
   b. Atmospheric conditions (recipe and ingredients)
   c. Damage that occurred and important statistics

Laboratory 13

Hurricanes: Digging into the Archives

Introduction

Tropical cyclones and hurricanes threaten US coastlines every summer and fall producing heavy rains, high winds, and damaging storm surges. This laboratory activity will use the National Oceanic and Atmospheric Administration (NOAA) National Hurricane Center (NHC) archives as a primary source to gather information about a deadly or damaging US landfalling hurricane. The NHC is located in Miami, Florida on the campus of Miami International University. The mission of the NHC is to save lives and mitigate property loss. This is accomplished through the issuing of timely and accurate watches, warnings, and forecasts. The NHC staff also provides detailed analyses of past events, archives, which we will access in this laboratory activity. The goal of this activity is to use a specific event to better understand tropical storm development.

Know Before You Go

Prior to completing the laboratory activity, you should review Chapter 11 Tropical Weather, Part II: Hurricanes in *A World of Weather: Fundamentals of Meteorology* and answer the following questions.

a. In your own words, describe the "ingredients" needed for tropical storm development.

b. Define the following:

Tropical depression:

Tropical storm:

Hurricane:

Extratropical storm:

c. Refer to Figure 11.52 in Chapter 11 Tropical Weather, Part II: Hurricanes in *A World of Weather: Fundamentals of Meteorology* and explain why the highest storm surge typically found in the right-front quadrant of a landfalling hurricane? Define right-front quadrant in your own words.

d. Using an Internet search engine, library reference book, or other methods, look up three different hurricane events that made landfall and significantly impacted the United States between 1995 and the previous calendar year. List the three potential events here. The goal will be for each student or group to cover a different event.

Get the Data

1. Choose one of the events above for your focus. Your instructor may assist with this process to ensure different events are covered or may direct the entire class to one particular event. List your event here:

2. Go to the NOAA National Hurricane Center Archive page at https://www.nhc.noaa.gov/data/tcr/.
3. Search for your event by clicking the appropriate year and then select the PDF file associated with that event.
4. Each archive report contains the following sections:
   a. Synoptic History
   b. Meteorological Statistics
   c. Casualty and Damage Statistics
   d. Forecast Warning and Critique
   e. Tables, Charts, Maps, and Diagrams
5. Read through all sections of the report and summarize the following:
   a. Synoptic history with special focus on "ingredients" for tropical storm development.
   b. Storm track through time including all landfall locations.
   c. Key meteorological statistics.
   d. Important casualty and damage statistics.

e. Did anything stand out in the Forecast Warning and Critique? State the key take away point.
f. Save the figures showing wind speed and pressure throughout time.

6. Use an Internet search engine to find photos, news articles, or other first-person accounts of the event.

Apply Your Knowledge

1. Share your knowledge of this event with others by preparing a Video Blog, Text Blog, or Powerpoint presentation of your event. Your instructor may provide further information; be sure to include all of the information summarized in "Get the Data" Questions 5 and 6.

Part

III

Hands-on Activities and Assignments

Laboratory

14

Home Analysis

Introduction

The apparent path of the sun varies throughout the year, affecting both the location along the horizon at sunrise and sunset and the noontime angle of the sun. Due to the tilt of the Earth there are seasonal changes in the length of daylight and intensity of the sunlight that reaches the surface. For those of us who reside outside the tropics, these changes in length of day and solar intensity can be quite dramatic. The farther we move from the Equator, the more dramatic the variations in length of day and solar intensity throughout the year.

As the sun's apparent path in the sky changes throughout the year (Figure 14.1), you may notice changes in your home or office environment. For example, large windows on the south-facing side of a home provide ample light and solar heating, typically, to reduce heating during the warm summer months large overhangs will be placed over the windows. During the winter months, especially at high latitudes, the overhangs will not shield the sun and the low sun angle will provide additional solar heating. Deciduous trees that lose their leaves in winter also provide a similar affect as the overhangs, shielding the home in the summer when additional solar heating would increase the indoor temperature too much and allowing sunlight to enter the home in winter when additional heating is necessary. Buildings with abundant windows on the north-facing side may experience colder rooms during winter months when winds come from a more northerly direction. Simple planning in home and

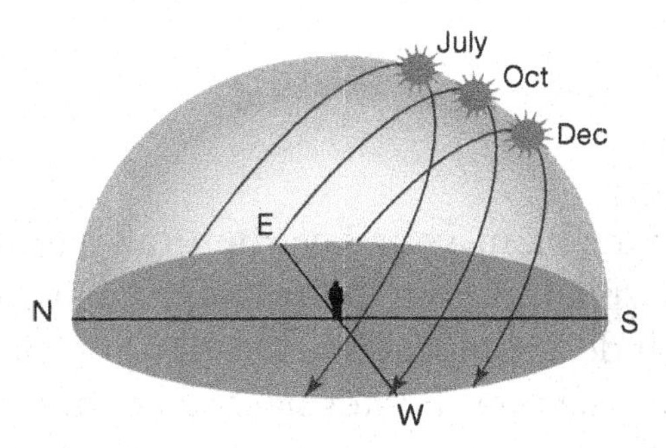

Figure 14.1. Apparent path of the sun in the Northern hemisphere mid-latitudes at various times throughout the year.

office design can save money on home heating and cooling bills. Bedrooms on the northern facing side of the home tend to be cooler and more comfortable for sleeping throughout the summer months.

This laboratory assignment will give you an opportunity to apply your knowledge of the apparent path of the sun to the heating and cooling of a space you are well familiar with, your home, office, or apartment building.

Know Before You Go

Prior to completing the laboratory activity, you should review Chapter 3 Global and Local Controllers of Temperature in *World of Weather: Fundamentals of Meteorology* and complete the following questions:

a. In what direction would you expect to find sunrise in high Northern Hemisphere middle latitudes near the time of the Winter Solstice?

b. In which direction would you expect to find sunset in the high Northern Hemisphere middle latitudes near the time of the Summer Solstice?

c. Draw a diagram of the apparent path of the sun for a location in the Northern Hemisphere mid-latitudes; be sure to label North, South, East, and West. You should draw a line to represent the apparent path of the sun for the time near the Winter Solstice, the Equinox, and the Summer Solstice.

d. On a clean sheet of paper or in your favorite drawing/illustration program, draw a basic sketch of the floorplan of your house/office/apartment, see Figure 14.2 for an example. Be sure to include a compass, the locations of windows, trees, overhangs, and other features, which impact your home's natural heating and cooling.

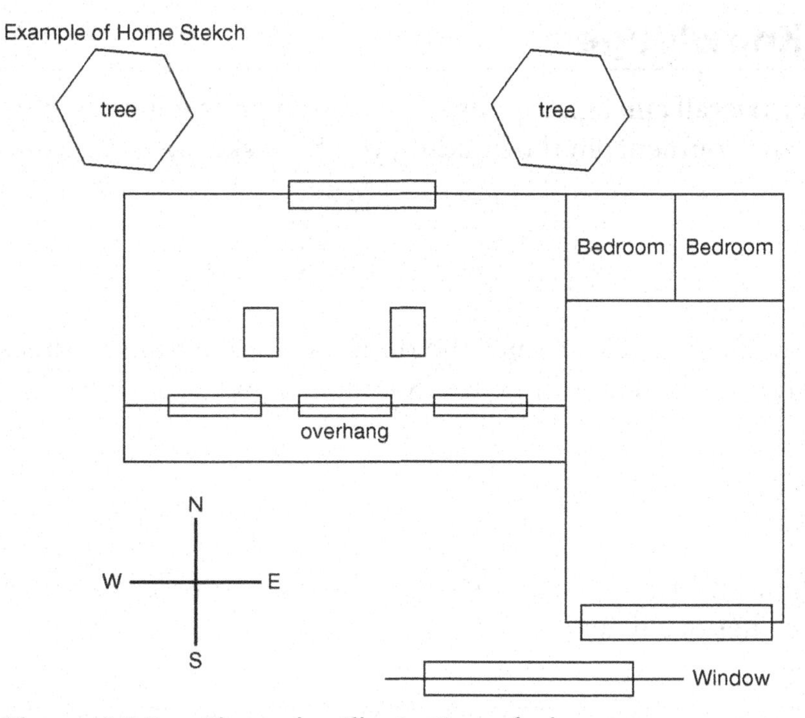

Figure 14.2. Floor plan illustration of a home.

Source: Kennie Leet.

Get the Data

1. On your sketch of your home, double check to be sure you have included the compass, windows, overhangs, trees, and other important features.

2. In which compass direction do the majority of your windows face?

3. Are there any features such as overhangs or trees that help shade south-facing windows in summer?

4. During the winter months, describe naturally warmer and colder places in the building you have sketched.

5. During the summer months, describe naturally warmer and colder places in the building you have sketched.

Apply Your Knowledge

1. Describe the overall efficiencies (times the design or orientation of this space improves the indoor environment) in the building you have sketched, example below.

2. Describe any inefficiencies (times the design or orientation of this space reduces the comfort of the indoor environment), example below.

3. Based on your findings in this activity, are there any simple changes you could make to improve the energy efficiency of the space?

Apply Your Knowledge – Example

1. The home in Figure 14.1 was designed to maximize the energy efficiency of the natural path of the sun. The home is a ranch-style home with one story partially underground with a walkout basement. Large windows are all along the south-facing side of the home with large overhangs, these overhangs shade the windows and home in summer and allow sunlight to enter in winter. In fact, on sunny days, very little additional (fossil fuel) heating is needed, even in winter. There are very few north-facing windows which also keep the home warmer in winter. The bedrooms on the north-facing wall have only east- or west-facing windows, keeping them warmer throughout the winter months and cooler in summer.
2. The home in Figure 14.1 had several owners since its initial construction and one owner decided to install skylights in the main living area on the south-facing side of the roof. While the skylights provided additional sunlight in winter, they made the home into a solar oven in summer; often indoor temperatures (without air conditioning) would exceed 85°F! Future owners removed these skylights and summer time indoor air temperatures have dropped by 5°F–10°F! The master bedroom is also on the south-facing side of the home with large windows with no overhang, this portion of the home sees much greater temperature swings, with lots of additional heat on sunny days and high heat loss (most likely due to poor insulation and its location over the garage) on cloudy days.

Laboratory 15

Snowflakes

Introduction

Snowflakes are beautiful and delicate forms of precipitation, Figure 15.1.

© Alexey Kljatov/Shutterstock.com

Figure 15.1. Snowflake.

If you are lucky enough to live in colder climates you may have an opportunity to catch and photograph snowflakes to observe this natural beauty and try to understand the environmental conditions that led to its formation. Wilson Bentley was the first known American to photograph snowflakes in great detail, taking over 5000 images in his lifetime at his home in Jericho, Vermont. Much of his collection can be viewed at the Jericho Historical Society in Jericho, Vermont and through the Buffalo Museum of Science, online collection at http://bentley.sciencebuff.org/collection.htm. More recently, physics professor Kenneth Libbrecht has utilized modern camera equipment to produce gorgeous snowflake photographs. His photographs are often used in coffee table books and even by the United States Postal Service in 2006 for the holiday stamp collection, information on his collections can be found at www.snowcrystals.com.

Know Before You Go

Prior to completing the laboratory activity, you should review Chapter 16 Winter Weather in *World of Weather: Fundamentals of Meteorology* and read the following article "How Snowflakes Get Their Shapes" at http://earthsky.org/earth/how-do-snowflakes-get-their-shape. Once you have read the article, complete the following questions:

a. Draw a simple diagram showing the type of snowflake formed at different temperatures.

b. Describe the ice nuclei process, and its relation to snowflake formation.

Figure 15.2. Snow pellets.

c. Figure 15.2 shows snow pellets, called graupel. Describe the conditions needed for graupel to form.

Get the Data

Option 1: Chilled Microscope and Snowfall

Supplies Needed:
Microscope (with photograph capability if available), glass slides, wool or felt dark mitten or cloth

Procedure:

1. Place all equipment outside protected under an overhang or porch to chill equipment but protect it from moisture.
2. Place your dark cloth in a place where snowflakes will fall on it.
3. Use a toothpick or small paintbrush to transfer snowflake from the cloth to the glass slide. Alternatively if slide is cold enough you can try to collect directly on the slide.
4. View the snowflake on the microscope and take photographs if you have the ability. If snowflakes are melting too quickly either the air temperature is too great or the equipment was not chilled enough.
5. Record all observations in Table 15.1, make additional copies if needed.

Option 2: Quality Cell Phone Camera and Snowfall

Supplies Needed: Cell phone camera, wool or felt dark mitten or cloth
Optional Supplies: Macrophotography camera attachment or jewelers loupe

Procedure:

1. Place all equipment outside protected under an overhang or porch to chill equipment but protect it from moisture.
2. Place your dark cloth in a place where snowflakes will fall on it.
3. Use your cell phone camera to take up close photos of the snowflakes. If you have a macrolens attachment for your phone, you can also use that. Example, Figure 15.3.

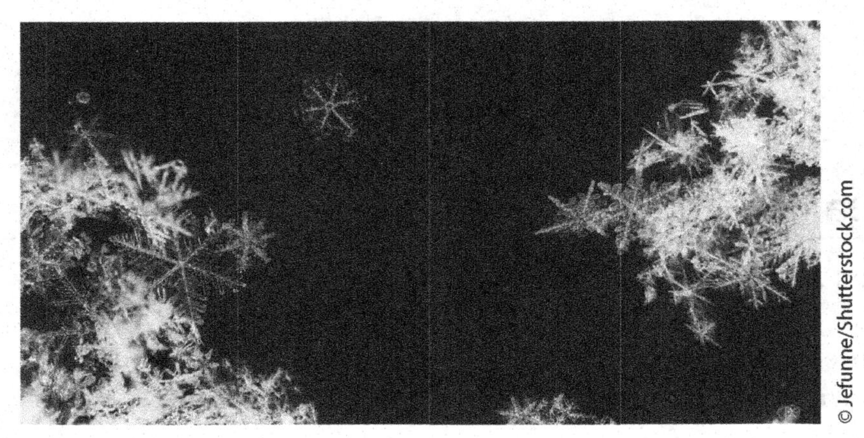

Figure 15.3. Real snowflakes.

4. Record all observations in Table 15.1, make additional copies if needed.

Option 3: Preserve Snowflakes

Supplies Needed:
Liquid super glue, glass slides and cover slips, wool or felt dark mitten or cloth

Procedure:

1. Place all equipment outside protected under an overhang or porch to chill equipment but protect it from moisture.
2. Place your dark cloth in a place where snowflakes will fall on it.
3. Use a toothpick or small paintbrush to transfer snowflake from the cloth to the glass slide.
4. Place a drop of super glue on top of the snowflake then cover with a cover slip.
5. Place the entire slide into a freezer for up to 48 hours. Remove the slide from the freezer, the impression of the snowflake will remain in the superglue.
6. Bring slides into the laboratory for observation under microscopes with photograph capabilities. Photograph each slide and record all observations in Table 15.1, make additional copies if needed.

For all options:

1. Record the date and time of the snowflake collection.
2. Save a screenshot of the Doppler Radar image from close to the time of collection.
3. Save a screenshot or image file of the 850 or 750 mb upper air temperature map.

Table 15.1. Snowflake Observation Records

Date and Time of Observation: **Name:**

Current Conditions:

Temperature:	
Dew-Point Temperature:	
Pressure:	
Pressure Tendency:	
Cloud Cover:	
Present Weather:	
Wind Direction:	
Wind Speed:	
Visibility:	
Other/Qualitative Observations:	

Snowflake Observations:

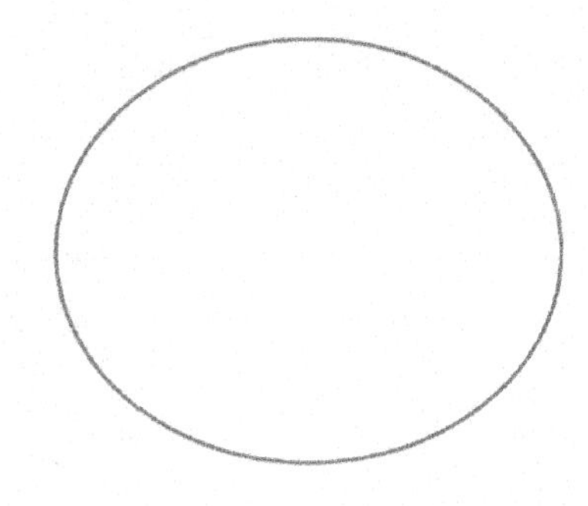

Type of Snowflake:

Type of Snowflake:

Apply Your Knowledge

1. What features did you observe on your snowflakes?

2. What inferences can you make about the atmosphere today where the snowflakes formed? Think about the snowflakes that form at different temperatures, the snowflakes you observed, and what you know about the upper atmospheric temperatures. Be as specific as possible.

3. What challenges surprised you about collecting and imaging snowflakes?

Laboratory

Climate Change

16

Introduction

The evidence for a changing climate due to anthropogenic forces is unequivocal. This lab will use the latest Intergovernmental Panel on Climate Change (IPCC) report to help understand the current state of the climate, the components that influence global climate, and the modeling efforts being conducted to understand future climate changes. For additional information about the structure of the IPCC, please refer to the *IPCC Fact Sheet: What is the IPCC?* http://www.ipcc.ch/news_and_events/docs/factsheets/FS_what_ipcc.pdf.

Know Before You Go

Prior to completing the laboratory activity, you should review Chapter 18 The Human Impact on Weather and Climate in *A World of Weather: Fundamentals of Meteorology* and answer the following questions.

a. How have scientists measured atmospheric carbon dioxide prior to the International Geophysical Year 1958 when Charles Keeling began detailed measurements of atmospheric carbon dioxide at Mauna Loa in Hawaii and at the South Pole?

b. What other gases are considered greenhouse gases? How have they changed over time, refer to Figure 18.9 in Chapter 18 The Human Impact on Weather and Climate in *A World of Weather: Fundamentals of Meteorology.*

c. What is the urban heat island effect?

d. What is a GCM?

e. How do volcanic eruptions influence climate?

Get the Data

1. Access the Intergovernmental Panel on Climate Change (IPCC) 5th report (or newer if available) at http://www.ipcc.ch/report/ar5/wg1/.
2. Click on the "Summary for Policymakers (SPM)".
3. Read through the summary.
4. You will notice that the report is divided into sections and begins with the current status of the climate, commenting on observed changes in the climate system. The report then discusses climate modeling efforts and expected changes based on climate models.
5. You, individually or in a group, will be assigned an aspect of the climate system, such as atmosphere, ocean, cryosphere, sea level, and biogeochemical cycles.
   a. Assigned topic: ______________________________
6. Using Chapter 18 The Human Impact on Weather and Climate in *A World of Weather: Fundamentals of Meteorology* and the *IPCC 5th Report: Summary for Policymakers (SPM),* summarize both the observed changes for your assigned system and the expected future changes.
7. Access the Intergovernmental Panel on Climate Change (IPCC) 5th report (or newer if available) at http://www.ipcc.ch/report/ar5/wg1/.
8. Select "All Graphics"
9. Browse graphics by chapter, note the graphics follow the full report chapters. You may access the full report on the same page for additional information on your topic. Select several images that capture the main idea in your section. Be sure to select images that you are comfortable explaining to the class, ones you understand. You may also refer to the full report for the figure caption and in text description.

Apply Your Knowledge

1. Develop your summary and selected images into a poster to present to the class.
   a. Set a custom presentation size in PowerPoint to 36" × 36" for your poster. Place your images and text in a meaningful and organized way on the single slide. Be sure to check your slide in 100% view to ensure text is readable and images are clear. Your instructor may share examples of scientific poster styles to assist you with organization and formatting.
2. Post or print your poster.
3. Present your work to the class. Remember posters should be explained much in the same way you would prepare a traditional PowerPoint presentation.